THE VINE WHISPERER

A hig hug
from Sicily
to
Niche

[signature]

THE VINE WHISPERER

A Sicilian Winemaker's Tale

Filippo Testa and Susannah Elliott

Translated from the Italian by Susannah Elliott

Matador
9 Priory Business Park,
Wistow Road, Kibworth Beauchamp,
Leicestershire. LE8 0RX
Tel: 0116 279 2299
Email: books@troubador.co.uk
Web: www.troubador.co.uk/matador
Twitter: @matadorbooks

ISBN 978 1788035 330

British Library Cataloguing in Publication Data.
A catalogue record for this book is available from the British Library.

Printed and bound in the UK by TJ International, Padstow, Cornwall
Typeset in 11pt Aldine401 BT by Troubador Publishing Ltd, Leicester, UK

Matador is an imprint of Troubador Publishing Ltd

Cover design by David Caines

It's hot
But the wind is picking up

The vines are glad
They say to the wind
I breathe
I live
Through you

ONE

My first memory of the family vineyards – the Azienda Tarantola – dates back to 1955. My mother, father, brother and I were being driven into the hills above Alcamo by horse and cart. There were cars in Sicily at the time, but most roads in the country were dirt tracks strewn with rocks and wild flowers that turned into rivers of ochre mud in the rain. They were not designed, in other words, for the modern motor car.

So the family was brought up to the vineyards in a *carretto*. A *carretto* is a traditional Sicilian cart, hand-painted in a myriad of colours – the carousel of colours that represent our lives. The carretto was a cheerful distraction on what would otherwise have been a long, uncomfortable journey, especially for my brother and me. Leaning over the wooden boards, watching as the painted sides of our carretto mingled with the glow of the hot evening countryside, was an unforgettable experience.

As soon as you left Alcamo and emerged into open land the way was pockmarked, and on one particular occasion the *carretto* drove over a crater and lurched violently to the side. I slipped like a fish out of my mother's arms, fell into the road and cracked open my delicate one-year-old skull. My mother was very distressed. She obviously thought it was her fault although of course it wasn't. Blood poured out of my head and the coachman hollered at his horses and drove them at breakneck speed to the farm.

There were many families living in the cluster of buildings around our farm at the time. The men were out working in the fields so only the women were at home – chopping, cooking, cleaning, dusting, polishing, sweeping … As soon as we arrived the coachman ran through the yard shouting in Sicilian: '*U figghiu du conte si rumpiu a testa!*' ('The count's son has cracked his skull!') Shouting it loud. And hearing that shout all the women hurried out of their houses to help, because in Sicily helping others is a passion. We do everything we can to assist someone in distress; it's in our nature. The women grabbed me, washed my head, and started to squeeze lemon juice onto the wound – from lemons snatched in seconds from the trees and torn open with their bare hands. They bandaged my head, binding it with jute, soaked the bandage with more lemon juice, and waited until the bitter-smelling astringent had drenched the wound before letting me and my mother leave the yard and continue our way up to the farmhouse.

A few days later the wound healed perfectly, so perfectly that when my mother recounted the story, as she did many times during my life, she would laugh and joke and say that she had thought me no better than dead, because the cut in my head was so deep and so long, but that the natural surgery of the countryside, the Sicilian lemon juice, had worked a miracle.

Maybe it was in that moment of pain, a pain that I can hardly remember, a pain that I probably wasn't fully aware of because I was too young, although I obviously cried a great deal, maybe it was in that moment that my love for the Azienda Tarantola was born.

My first wail of entry into the countryside.

Every harvest, almost religiously, we travelled the same road. Eventually motor cars became more robust and the roads were asphalted, so instead of taking a *carretto* we drove into the country. But whether by cart or by car it was a procession of pilgrimage, winding its way from Palermo to Alcamo and arriving, dirt-strewn and thirsty, at Tarantola.

The land at Tarantola has been owned by the Testa family for generations. Originally the hills were grazed, and the lower fields cultivated with durum wheat. Vineyards were first planted at Tarantola in the nineteenth century and there have been vines on the estate ever since.

My father always held that sharecropping was the best way of working the land. The landowner provided the terrain, the sharecroppers provided the labour and the product of the harvest was divided in half. The sharecroppers received a half-share of the produce rather than payment – so of course it was in their interest to make sure that the vines were productive.

Sharecroppers played an important role for aristocratic proprietors at the time. It was unthinkable for anyone who owned more than two or three hundred hectares not to have sharecroppers and certainly for an elderly man like my father, who would never have had the capacity to manage the vineyards, the system was indispensible. With sharecroppers on the land he could stay in Palermo for most of the year and arrive at Tarantola only for the harvest – to celebrate the work done for him by others.

Even though the landowner was always the landowner and the worker always the worker, harvest was a time of communal celebration. In those days grapes matured relatively late, about halfway through September, not like the varieties we have now – Chardonnay, Nero d'Avola, Syrah – which are fully mature by mid August. At that time there was only one vine, one type of grape, and the grape was called Catarratto. The Catarratto was the prince on the hills of Alcamo. Resistant to high temperatures, resistant to the September rains – which were frequent at the time – the Catarratto was handsome, blond, full of light and colour and, most importantly, blessed with a high sugar content.

In years when the harvest was plentiful and the grape must abundant, musicians came to the farm to take part in the autumn celebrations and everybody danced. Out on the hills above Alcamo you can hear the hoot of an owl for miles around, so, when the band started to play, down from the hills came a swarm of people – workers from other estates, families dressed in their Sunday best – scampering through the vineyards to join in the unforgettable annual ritual, the Festival of the Harvest. The band played light, frivolous music with a simple beat that seeped into you. Sicilian melodies and ballads in dialect trilled through the cool night air, and the revellers, fuelled by wine, song, *sfincione*, cheese and sweets, danced until dawn. Even my father, who seemed ancient when I was young, looking out of the window and seeing everyone jostling and joking and laughing, rushed down into the yard to dance with my mother in the dust.

The root of my name, Filippo, is a combination of the Greek words *philos* and *hippos*, which together mean 'lover of horse'. My first passion was for horses – I loved them, I thought, more than I loved myself. Nobody owned tractors when I was a child so the land was worked by horses, and we had more than twenty of them on the farm. In those days you didn't take a horse out for fresh air and exercise, or for the joy of galloping through the fields, or to escape into the cool of the mountains. You took a horse out for one reason and one reason only: to work.

When I was about eleven or twelve I wanted to be a *carriatore*. A *carriatore* in Sicily is the person who rides into the fields during the harvest to collect the grapes. My parents didn't want me to be a *carriatore* – you are the son of the owner, you don't work in the fields – but I was desperate to be part of it. I wanted to take my place with all the other little boys of the neighbourhood – 'little' because they always put the lightest ones on the horses. I longed to join in with the ritual of the harvest and hold my head high on a Sicilian mare.

I took myself down to the stables and watched while the other boys led their fillies out at the beginning of the day and brought them back, tired and sweating, into the yard at dusk. In front of the stables was a little bank of sand. I stared as the horses sank themselves down and rolled over on the ground – kicking their legs in the air, grinding granules of sand into their fur and throwing up dusty clouds. Later, I would steal into the stalls before dinner and drop a grape into each hay bag, buying myself a few seconds of intimacy, whispering sweet nothings into impatient ears.

Eventually my parents gave in.

I rode out early in the morning, climbed up the hill, watched while the farm workers filled my baskets with bunches of grapes and wobbled back down to the winery with a bulging load. Outside the winery stood a line of presses operated by mules, patient beasts who trudged round and round all day on their long, interminable journey. Each bunch was tossed into the mouth of a press to be crushed. I loved seeing the must squeezed out of the grapes, the juice slithering into the vats. Even though I was only small I jumped down to help and told myself that one tiny drop in those great swirling vats bore my signature.

At nine o'clock all the farm workers stopped to eat and I was handed a meagre breakfast – a salted sardine and a little piece of bread. The other boys got half a sardine – I got a whole one because I was the son of the count. The workers would eat tomato and olive salad, dressed with fresh olive oil, vinegar and water. Sometimes they would give me some of their salad dressing to dip my bread into. It tasted wonderful. Workers in the country always thought city people were stupid, and I was a city boy, so that breakfast had the weight of a trophy in my hands because I knew what it meant. It meant that I had worked hard and that my work was considered good. If you didn't work hard and your work wasn't good, you didn't get breakfast.

I remember the farm workers – peasants born and

brought up on the land, their skin shrivelled by long days in the sun. They laboured, bent or twisted, from seven in the morning until five in the evening. When you took one of their hands it was like touching the bark of a tree. The hoe, the pick, all the tools of the countryside had defined the structure of their hands. Their limbs were shaped by labour, hard, manual labour, the kind of labour that has slowly diminished with the coming of the tractor.

Sometimes I meet the sons of those peasants – boys who have grown up to become engineers, solicitors, even business consultants. When we talk about old times they always say the same thing: my parents were poor and we suffered but I think of my childhood days in the countryside as the most precious days of my life.

The swinging movement of the horse under my weight, with its two great baskets creaking on either side; the heady smell of the grape must; the heat of the sun; the sticky, grape-sugary feel of my hands – these memories have stayed with me throughout my life. They are as clear in my mind as pebbles at the bottom of a limpid blue pool.

My father, the Conte Testa, was a *gran signore*, a nobleman. I hardly knew him – he married late in life, and by the time I was born he was nearly sixty. I find it difficult to paint an accurate picture of his character – there are so many gaps and inconsistencies in my memory of him. By repute he was enormously charming and was held in great esteem by everyone around him. He dressed elegantly and almost always wore a trilby whenever he went out into the street, in a manner befitting a count. I, however, have an abiding image of him in shorts. I hated shorts.

Memories that linger from my childhood are linked to the summer – swimming in cool seawater, kicking a football around on the beach, playing silly games in the waves. My father never came to the beach – he never came for a swim with me, he never played football – he had no enthusiasm for games or sport, he wasn't interested in any of the things that interested me.

He was a man of few words who could strike fear into your heart with a look – not because he meant you any harm but because he had such expressive eyes. Maybe that was why he didn't speak much, because his eyes spoke for him. He was also very spoilt. I remember a story told by my aunt, his sister, the beloved Carmelina whom we called Zia Lina. Before my father was married, when he was still living at home with his mother and his sisters, he used to hold the entire household in his thrall. It was his habit to come home for lunch every day and he insisted that his pasta should be served to him hot and al dente the minute he walked through the door. But he never told anyone what time he was coming home – nobody knew – was it going to be one o'clock, two o'clock? So his sisters used to stand on the balcony of the Palazzo Testa on the Via Victor Emmanuele, scanning the long avenue in the midday sunlight for his figure. As soon as they spotted him in the distance, they would run into the kitchen and lower the pasta into the boiling water so that when he arrived it would be perfectly cooked. Maybe he was selfish, maybe he was even a little bit cruel, or maybe he was simply the product of a different era. Either way, the truth is that Lina absolutely adored him, as did everyone in the family.

My father was not a man of business. He believed things would work themselves out without any particular intervention from him. His byword in life was 'no'. Mr No. 'No' to everything, whatever it was, accompanied by a list of excuses that had no reason or rhyme. At a certain period in his life it appears he had a nervous breakdown, although no one ever called it that, which is possibly why his response to everything was: I can't, it's not the right time, we can't manage it, there's no point, we should just sell everything.

We should sell everything.

When I was about four or five years old, my father's cousin got into financial difficulty and said to my father: 'Listen, I need to raise a bit of money and I'm thinking of selling the first floor of the palazzo. Why don't you buy it? I'll sell it to you at a reasonable price and at least that way it will stay in the family.' My father wouldn't buy. He said that it wouldn't be right for him to buy from his cousin. Why? Because people would say that he was profiting from his cousin's misfortune.

My mother tried to help him with the family affairs. She suggested they invest money and buy a house next to the sea. She suggested they invest in the land and replant the vineyards. She suggested that they start bottling the wine. All her suggestions fell on deaf ears.

Wine was our principle form of income, so even though my father managed to detach himself from most aspects of the family business he had no choice but to concentrate on the comings and goings of the wine market. During the winter, the period when the wine was sold, we would be inundated by a battery of telephone calls from wine brokers making offers. As well as having a wine cellar at the farm, we had a wine warehouse in Alcamo and at the height of the selling season I used to accompany my father there. We would drive to Alcamo in a beautiful red car. Even at the age of eight I knew he wasn't a good driver, in fact I remember squirming in my seat because he was so absent-minded on the road. But then his father, my grandfather, owned a train carriage. If he wanted to go anywhere – to Rome, say, with the family – he would arrange to have the carriage attached to the back of a train and off they would go – travelling to Rome in their own private quarters. So perhaps my father wasn't keen on driving because he saw himself as the sort of man who should have a train carriage.

At that time everyone made wine in the Alcamo region and Alcamo town in winter was a buzzing wine exchange – full of brokers, negotiating in every cafe. I would eat granita with brioche while my father and the brokers chewed the fat over a coffee, two coffees, three coffees, and talked money. I was a devourer of sweets and ice creams so I never paid much attention to the conversation because all I was thinking about was my granita, but I do remember the early-morning starts, rising at five thirty, and the hours taken for the buyers' trucks to load up the wine once it was sold. To transfer wine from our tanks into six or seven trucks using hand pumps took an entire day. It was the most important, but for me the most boring, event of the year. So many people, the heady whiff of alcohol everywhere, the cold spick and span of the wine cellar – its entire floor scoured the minute a single drop of wine fell on the ground.

The profitability of a vineyard follows a curve – a parabola of productivity. Initially, when the vines are planted, you go through a period of loss. Gradually, as the yield increases, the profits rise until you reach a peak and are in a state of equilibrium – the years of maximum profitability. After several years of production, however, the vines start producing less grapes and finally they produce so little that you make no profit from them at all. If you don't take the matter in hand and replace the vines at exactly the right point, you lose money.

My father was brilliant at losing money because he never wanted to take anything in hand – his modus vivendi being 'do nothing' – and so the vines became less and less productive until they were producing barely a grape. The sharecroppers were on their knees, begging him for permission to dig up the old vines and plant new ones, but his response was always: 'No, not this year, not this year.'

M any people would come to the farm, wanting to see the Conte Testa. Some of them were labourers asking for work. Some of them were respectable, even distinguished visitors from the region. But some were what I will call 'personages' – strange, formal figures, dressed, for the most part, entirely in black.

I used to watch them from the window, these figures, as they discoursed with my father – one man in particular. He and my father would walk up and down the little tree-lined road leading to the farmhouse – up, and down, up, and down. Later, at the dinner table, when I asked my father what on earth they had been talking about as they walked up, and down, up, and down, he would simply reply: 'Oh, he wanted to know if I needed anyone, any workers on the farm, you know …'

I came to know the personages by name. Women working in the farmhouse would discuss their arrival, or they would be referred to in conversations in the yard. My father had his newspaper delivered from Alcamo every day – he read it after coffee in the morning and left it in the wastepaper basket in his office. When he retired for his siesta in the afternoon my mother would enter the office to tidy his desk and give it some semblance of order and she would often ask me to empty the wastepaper basket. One day, when I was old enough to read, and almost old enough to understand what I read, instead of throwing the paper into the dustbin I took it into the kitchen, smoothed it out on the table and tried to decipher the tiny black-and-white text. On the front page was an article about the power struggles of the local Mafia. The surnames listed were familiar to me. I called my brother over and pointed them out to him, hoping that he would explain why the names we now knew so well were in the paper. My brother was almost twice my height and he towered above me. Pressing his hands down on my shoulders, he peered over my head, scanned the article and gave a disinterested grunt before walking away.

Gradually I began to understand. The personages whose names I now spotted in the papers on a regular basis were not visiting out of courtesy, they were visiting for a reason: 'Signor Testa, there's a boy who needs work – why don't you take him on for a while, try him out, as a favour to me …?' So many people 'taken on', especially during the harvest, who did no work whatsoever, certainly not on the harvest. They were paid to work on the harvest but they had no intention of working on the harvest because they were working on something quite different.

At first this 'employment' only went on for about twenty days, twenty-five days at most, during the autumn season. However, the time came when we were also obliged to take people on in the winter. One young man sticks in my memory. He was not taken on as a labourer but as a guard: someone to keep an eye on the estate and the workers, and make sure that everything was in order while the family was away. After a couple of months this guard stepped out of line. My parents had decided to bring the family up to the farm for the weekend, possibly unannounced, and my mother, as she was unpacking in the bedroom, found a gun lying on the marital bed. When the guard turned up at the house a few hours later my father asked him why the gun was there. The guard replied: 'Ah. Yes. I came in last night because I heard some strange noises, and I had to investigate your bedroom to make sure there were no intruders...' along with some other equally unlikely stories.

My father picked up the telephone. He informed the 'personage' what had happened and told him in no uncertain terms that he found the guard's behaviour both ignorant and unacceptable. 'I am not happy – one just does not do that sort of thing. I pay the man to look after the farm and to keep an eye on the workers. I do not pay him to sleep in my bed and play the proprietor!'

The 'personage' came to call. This time the afternoon stroll up and down the road lasted a little longer than usual. Normally it went on for about twenty minutes, half an hour at the most, finishing with a coffee. This one lasted for over an hour. My father was visibly agitated and I heard him raise his voice several times. The personage listened impassively; he didn't say a word. He was taking it all in – the damage that had been done to his reputation with my father and, more importantly, much, much more importantly, the offence that had been committed against himself.

Despite the rather heightened tone of the conversation, the closing coffee-drinking ritual was still observed – accompanied by a barrage of hugs and kisses and a sentence that I heard distinctly: 'Signor Conte, do not worry yourself, we will deal with it.' My father clearly expected the guard to receive a severe reprimand

and sharpen up his behaviour so that they could all make a fresh start.

The next day the guard went missing. I remember my father coming in to the kitchen and saying to my mother: 'Bebè,' (he called her bebè or bambi, short for bambina) 'Bebè, you know that guard? Well, he's disappeared.' And my mother, so naive, so terribly naive, said: 'Disappeared? How can a man just disappear? Impossible. He must have gone away somewhere.' To which my father replied: 'No, he's disappeared.'

They call it *lupara bianca* – white shotgun. *Lupara bianca* is the term used when someone is murdered but you never find the body.

٢

TWO

My mother's name was Caterina. She was a shapely woman, almond-faced, with thick, dark, wavy but well-coiffured hair. She was not what you might call a supermodel, but to me she was beautiful. I felt proud walking by her side. Walking by her side was like stepping over the keys of a piano – there were white keys and black keys, major notes and minor notes. And the perfume of flowers everywhere.

Caterina loved flowers and flowers loved her. Flowers were her way of expressing herself, her zest for life. The balconies of our house were among the most verdant in the city – a suspended haven of foliage.

In Palermo we lived in the Palazzo Testa, most of which belonged to my father's cousin. In common with other palazzi there was a *piano nobile* – the principle, grand living quarters on the first floor. My father's cousin lived on the *piano nobile* and we lived in the apartment above. My mother walked everywhere with me when I was young – to school, to the shops, to the seafront. Before we left she would check my appearance, wipe away a smear of dirt or food, straighten anything that was askew, take hold of my hand and lead me out of the door. We had to take a rickety little lift down to the street that was operated by a short, surly porter. Every time we got into the lift my mother would say sweetly to the porter, '*Buona Mattina*'. But he would never respond. In the afternoon or early evening we would return and as we got into the lift on the ground floor, my mother would say to the porter, '*Buona Sera*', and again the porter declined to respond. One day, after I had witnessed this small but somehow significant event countless times, I asked my mother: 'Why do you keep saying good morning and good evening to the porter when he never says anything back?' She replied: 'It doesn't matter if the porter responds or doesn't respond; what counts is that I show him my respect.'

I was very attached to my mother – she was my anchor, my reference point. When I was young and she went out to listen to a concert or a recital, I often used to pretend that I had been struck down with some terrible illness to make her come home early. Mamma was exceptionally ingenuous, she trusted everyone, so it was easy for me to deceive her. But, like me, she was anxious. At the age of fourteen I was given my first Vespina and I would ride around the city for hours and hours, coming home well after dark. My mother spent the whole evening standing on her perfumed balcony, watching as the twilight filtered through the fronds of the balustrade, waiting for me to come home.

I still meet people who talk about my mother. They comment on her elegance, her integrity, her commitment to her family and her sons, her grace. You never heard a rude word from her, and there was certainly never any sign that she was troubled by life's travails. If ever she frowned there was always a smile somewhere in view over the horizon. She distributed smiles to everyone, gifting moments of happiness to all she met.

It was not that Mamma had never experienced difficulty in her life. She had lived through the war, and as a young woman she had known poverty and hunger.

She once told me how she used to spend long evenings breaking her bread into crumbs, rolling the crumbs into balls with her fingers, and laying them out in a line to make herself feel as if the bread would last forever. But, like my father, she didn't often refer to the past. Both my father and my mother, for their own separate reasons, kept their early stories buried deep and avoided talking about them.

I often wondered if I would become like my mother, possess the qualities that she possessed, lead the life that she led, but I realised as I grew older that it would never happen – our characters were too different.

Caterina studied the piano at the Conservatorio Bellini in Palermo. She used to play in our apartment, sweetening the air with the sounds of Beethoven, Liszt, Schumann, Bach. She would practise and practise and then she would call me over to the piano to listen. Her favourite works were the études by Chopin – she played those masterpieces to perfection.

My mother played the piano the way she lived her life – with delicacy. There was something distinctive about her touch, her hands, her fingers as they caressed the keys. The old upright piano in our apartment could never do her justice. Some nights she would say that she was too tired to practice, but I would beg her to play and she, pliable and modest as she was, would sit down at the piano to please me. Notes cascaded in and out of my ears, lingering in my heart, pressing me into a world of sound and rhythm that had more in store for me than I could ever have imagined.

She tried to teach me, but, despite her constant remonstrations, I would only play with two fingers. She spent hours coaching me, telling me that only with dedication, only by going over the most challenging sections a hundred, two hundred times, only with absolute determination and without surrender would I succeed in overcoming my obstacles. She tried to help me understand that the moments when everything falls apart are the moments when you learn the most. I remember those lessons with fondness – I would spend hours tinkering away on the keyboard, twisting the exercises and making up scales, trying to make sense of it all. My mother would listen and move to and from the balcony, pruning the roses, watering the plants, coming back into the room to praise me or correct me. Occasionally a thought came into her mind and she would stop to talk, and sometimes the conversation drifted towards her time studying at the conservatorio, but there were traces of bitterness buried in the memory so she would never dwell on it for long.

As I grew older I started to practice on my own. Conjuring up what felt like an enormous concentration of willpower, I taught myself to use three, four, five fingers until eventually I brought each digit to life and forced it to work, labouring a kind of harmony out of the keys. I made half-hearted attempts to follow a score, but I could only stay with a sequence for a few seconds and so I began to explore other possibilities. I played from instinct, joining notes with notes, then adding more, making a tide of sound that rushed into the air and sucked back in on itself. Music started to possess me. It was a devil spitting fire inside me. I created out of nothing. I spent hours hammering away at the keys until, satisfied, I stood up, walked around, and then sat back down to begin all over again.

By chance I heard about two pianists, Keith Jarrett and Chick Corea. The first bowled me over with his improvisational prowess. I studied him incessantly, listened, read interviews, becoming more and more convinced that the true art was the art of improvisation and that anyone who could apply that art, even in everyday life, would be saved, nothing would stand in its way. I read a book, a sort of encyclopedia, recounting the story of jazz from its origins to the present day. I pored over that book as if it were the Gospel. I read over and over again the chapter about sounds moulded in the cotton fields. I studied the cotton pickers' songs, intoned to harmonise with the sweep and slice of the shears as the cotton stems were cut and the heavy crops dropped into baskets below. The Gospel introduced me to the earthbound form of rhythm and blues.

I resolved that, if ever I should play the piano professionally, I would play jazz. I didn't care about reading or writing music, I had no interest in improving on what others had written, it was the idea of improvisation that was gnawing at me. When you improvise you start with a tune, but then you slide into another gear and enter a mysterious world, a black space in which your hands are following an unknown course and you have no idea where it will take you. Jazz has a thousand colours. It enters you, leaves you, comes at you, pulls away again. It throws you up into the air, it slaps you down, it shatters you with sound and image, it leaves you with unforgettable sensations that will never return because when you improvise ... the thing about improvisation is that you create the moment and when that moment is over it is over. You cannot recreate it, and you cannot copy it. Like life.

I formed a band with some friends. We practiced in a small room in the basement of a house in Palermo and flirted with all the different genres – rock, jazz, blues, piano and drums, piano and percussion, piano and bass.

The others were less committed but I wanted to rehearse every night – I thought of nothing else, only music. The room we played in was hot and often, at the height of summer, my friends would quit, making excuses – they had to return home to eat with their parents, or visit their grandmothers, or finish a piece of work for college – when in reality they had arrangements to meet girls in front of the Teatro Massimo, or to drink iced salted lemonade on a bench overlooking the ferry port.

Sometimes I would carry on playing without them, for an hour or two, and then I would let myself out of the house and walk. Walk through Palermo. Palermo in the early hours. The windows of the city, shuttered against the heat, or possibly against something else, made deep holes in the night. Even the main streets, full of high tones and jostling traffic and flashing lights during the day, were still.

I walked for hours – inhabiting the darkness – past palaces in the historic centre still lying in ruins thirty years after the war because nobody had either the money or the will to rebuild them. We Palermitans are so used to being surrounded by rubble – be it Greek, or Roman, or medieval – that it seems normal to us to live among ruins. Under a bright moon the graffitied walls of the city looked like decaying teeth.

When I came home I would usually find my mother waiting for me. By this time it was too late for her to stand on the balcony so she sat on a little wooden chair near the balcony windows, with a red shawl around her. When I walked into the room she would stand up, kiss me on the cheek, and then retire to bed. Once or twice, knowing that I had been rehearsing, she would ask me how my rehearsal had gone and request that I play her something. I would leaf through a pile of scores jumbled at the foot of the piano – Johann Sebastian Bach on top of Chick Corea, Keith Jarrett next to Frédéric Chopin, Franz Liszt inside McCoy Tyner. Casting aside the classical pieces, I attacked the most complicated jazz piano sections I could lay my hands on. In the quiet of the dawn the notes of the piano sounded deafening, but neither of us cared.

E ventually our band worked up enough tunes to justify a gig, and we started to sell ourselves to local bars. Playing in public was petrifying – especially for me. I was the one breaking out into solo after the 'head', the first melody section, was over. I was the one improvising, weaving my way into the wilderness, and then rejoining the band and bringing us all back to the melody. I started to suffer from anxiety and stomach cramps. After our first gig I was confined to bed for three days with stabbing pains in my abdomen and a terrible, asphyxiating nausea.

Bookings were sporadic and, although we were well received, the gigs were mostly attended by friends and acquaintances who were as interested in talking to each other as they were in listening to us. I became frustrated with the group, and they with me. I never did the same thing during a set, or at least I started out in one direction and then changed everything. I was doing what I wanted to do – improvising in public and taking risks – but the risks that I was taking were wrong-footing the band even though, paradoxically, they made me feel safer.

Some members of the band started to experiment with drugs. This was not unusual among boys at the time, especially boys from privileged backgrounds who had a bit of cash at their disposal. Rehearsals became less and less disciplined, with the occasional flurries of inspiration sandwiched between hours of indolence. I left the band and played independently – wherever, whenever I could: during the interval of a cabaret, a solo piano slot in a bar, a set in a cinema with other musicians. I ignored phone calls from the band, I avoided all the places we frequented together and spoke to no one.

The anxiety increased, and the stomach cramps, this time with a vengeance. I was tussling with terrible, agonising needles of pain during the day and haunted by a festering depression at night. But I was also encountering something new – a rage that I never knew I had within me, a rage that made me despise the world I was living in, despise its passive acceptance of all that was evil, despise its inequalities, its mendacity, its sloth. I played with a new vigour, a vigour driven by frustration and passion. Anyone who knew me, who met me at that time, was bemused. I was unrecognisable – the cheerful, hearty young aristocrat had become thin, unshaven, dishevelled.

My mother began speaking to me in hushed tones, trying to coax out of me what was driving me insane, but I couldn't explain, neither to her nor to myself. I only knew that I had to fight my affliction and somehow succeed as a musician. I did everything in my power to launch that ship, to find that hallowed career. I recorded tracks on a cheap cassette player balanced on top of our old piano. I sent cassettes to every record company I could think of – mostly to companies in the north of Italy, the affluent North. I spoke to managers, to agents. I practised morning, noon and night. Eventually the owner of one of the clubs I was playing in sat down by the piano and offered me a drink. A free drink – that was a good sign. He told me that I had talent – there was a lot of work still to do and I needed to sort out my appearance and my manner onstage, but he was prepared to give me a chance. He would book me for one night a week – a regular appearance – and act as my agent, promoting me to his friends in the music business in return for a percentage of my earnings. If I was in agreement, he said, he would draw up a contract.

My playing was at its best – every ache of my muscles, every inch of my being was spewing itself out onto the keyboard. The moment had come, I was focused, I knew I was ready.

walking
listening
to my thoughts
my fears
the sound of footsteps
on the pavement
this sick city stinks of petrol
a heap of rubble
without trees
miserable until morning
knowing that the day has begun
not because the birds have started singing
but because the buses have started to run
never any darkness
never any night
constant cars
constant light
no air
even the wind here
is absent

luckily I'm listening to Keith Jarrett:
'Paris Concert'

THREE

The death of my father came suddenly but not unexpectedly. He died of lung cancer, mercifully quickly after his initial diagnosis. He had been suffering from mental and physical exhaustion for some time and in the last years of his life had abandoned everything, including the family business. My mother, unfortunately, knew nothing about the business because my father would never let her get anywhere near it. 'Bebè – business is not for you,' he used to say. Not surprisingly, when my father died, she showed no inclination to start learning how to do the accounts, how to plan, how to negotiate, how to forge deals, and so she began to echo his words: 'Not now, perhaps next year, I just can't face it right now ...'

I had never been interested in running the family business, but my elder brother announced soon after my father's death that he was travelling the world and would be gone for the foreseeable future, so I agreed to accompany my mother on her weekly trips to the farm to pay the workers.

The farm. Alcamo. The family vineyards – so beautiful and so rigorous – hot groves that in recent years I had only thought of as a holiday retreat – a lush, shady spot to hide in with some girlfriend or other. Suddenly it struck me that these vineyards were my responsibility. A burden that sat on my shoulders and my shoulders only. But I was still immature, with problems of my own and the promise of a new career. How could I take on a large, unwieldy, uncared for estate? How would I survive in the familiar and yet unknown, welcoming and yet hostile environment that was Tarantola? I had spent my life living and breathing the city – I knew nothing, really, about life in the countryside.

I decided to spend some time in Alcamo, the town that was nearest our vineyards. I strolled around of an evening, and met people who were prodigal with pieces of friendly advice. Embedded within all these pieces of friendly advice there was a single, faintly discernible thread: things aren't like they were in your father's time; everything is different now; you can't do it on your own; this is my advice that I give you like a brother; your family is practically bankrupt; the best thing for you now would be to sell. Who were these fine gentlemen, professing to be great admirers of my father, offering me coffee or granita in the Piazza Ciullo di Alcamo? Were they bankers perhaps? Is that why they knew so much about our family and our family's finances? No. They weren't bankers. What then? How did they know we were facing rack and ruin? I was so gullible. A little boy who could be twirled around on a string, and I was twirling, spinning like a top – so many slaps on the back, so many patronising smiles, nothing said with any seriousness, no, everything dismissed with a laugh. Weeks passed, and the pieces of friendly advice never changed.

My mother was becoming nervous. A family friend called in at the apartment in Palermo and sat me down. She spoke to me quietly. 'Your mother is getting old, you know that she has the right to live quietly, you have to understand that it is time for you to sell. There are people who are interested in buying – next week they will send a representative to make you an offer.'

'Who are these 'people'? And why, if they're so interested, don't they come themselves?'

'What does it matter?' was the reply. 'The important thing is to listen to what is offered and if all goes well you will hear from their solicitor.'

The representative came and made the offer: less than 50 per cent of the value of the land. It was not an offer, it was daylight robbery. I told my mother I wasn't interested, even when she tried to persuade me, saying: 'Surely it would be better to sell, we don't have the strength, and also I'm worried about you, you're young, you have a career ahead of you, why launch yourself into a world you don't understand? Let's accept the crumbs they're offering and be done with Tarantola, it has only lost us money, and created problems for us, and given us sorrow.'

I turned it over in my head. I thought and thought about what we should do. My mother and I decided to stay on the farm for a few days to meet the local bank manager, talk to a land agent and assess the condition of the estate and the buildings. How things had changed. The land that had once been the jewel in the family crown was now a graveyard of old, unproductive vines with only one thing ahead of them: extermination. We were in trouble – broken in spirit, broken as an estate, and broken financially.

In the evening my mother and I sat on the terrace overlooking the vineyards. I couldn't think of a way out. My mother couldn't think of a way out. There was one thing, however, that was becoming clear in my mind – that the son sitting next to his mother on the veranda, the young man who not so long ago had been a truculent, needy boy, was growing up second by second and asking himself – why should we sell if this has been our way of life for centuries? Wouldn't it be better to continue the family tradition, a tradition we were once so proud of?

On the spur of the moment I told my mother not to contact the land agent. I promised that I would pull myself together, settle down, and take on a job with a steady income that would allow me to try my hand at running the farm and see if I could turn things around.

The old vines stretched out in front of us as far as the eye could see. Silhouetted against the sun their stems were crooked and black. Farm buildings stood all around in a state of neglect and disrepair. But a breeze was blowing, the tiles of the terrace were giving off their residual warmth, and a soft, pregnant curve of olive trees above seemed to come closer, as if the hills themselves were trying to embrace us.

My mother looked suddenly very tired and alone. What else could she do, she said, but agree.

I started by reappropriating the family land and dispensing with the system of sharecropping. I made a pact with the sharecroppers and agreed that for three years they would pay no fees – they would take the produce of the harvest and any profits made would be theirs – but at the end of three years the land would return to us, to be farmed, in the future, by us. Some of the farmers objected – they came to me trying to haggle, or to demand an immediate transfer of their land for cash. Some thought they could convince me, young and ignorant as I was, to pay more than the land was worth, but I researched the market and paid what was fair.

I kept my word to my mother and took a full-time job in Palermo. A friend who specialised in computer technology asked me to work with him, programming business software – a nice, flexible position that would allow me to manage my own time and spend days at Tarantola when I needed to. I rang the club owner who had offered me a contract and told him that I was taking a break from jazz for a while, but as soon as I had 'sorted a few things out' I would be back in touch. We both knew that was a lie.

I made a decision to propose to a girl I had been seeing on and off for a while. Within a year we were married and living in our own apartment. Within two years she had given birth to our first child.

In the meantime I visited the farm at weekends, observed the movement of the seasons in the vineyards, talked to the sharecroppers who were still working on our land, listened to their advice, and sat on the terrace in the evening looking at it all.

The hills around Tarantola are known for their sunsets. The landscape is undulating, irregular, and when you climb the slope behind the farmhouse and look out over the valley, vineyards and olive groves in variegated shades of green and blue stretch out in front of you for miles. The crests of some of the smaller hillocks around are planted with a single pine tree that rises above the vegetation and as the sun sinks these hillocks become soft and skin-coloured, like the gently sloping breasts of a giant goddess. Clouds, lit up from below and glowing burnt orange and red, streak the sky above in curious shapes, and the vineyards around the farm are transformed into avenues of umber light.

Walking the land one night at sunset, surrounded by this mythical vision, I began to think again about the music of the cotton pickers. There was more to jazz than melody and rhythm. Jazz was the poetry of life, jazz reflected nature, jazz and nature were perfectly aligned. I decided that I wanted to be a jazz farmer. I wanted my vines to hear music, to love music. I wanted to listen to music as I walked through the vineyards – not on headphones but out loud. I wanted to listen to jazz as I looked over the grapes. A jazz farmer, I thought to myself, would know how to hear what his plants were telling him. If there was one lesson that I had learned from my days out in the fields as a *carriatore*, from the peasants I had watched as a young boy, from the baskets of vegetables so proudly gifted to the family by the farm workers, from my mother's lush and fragrant balcony, it was that plants thrive on one thing over and above any other. Not fertiliser. Not pesticide. Not the artificial or even organic products that man dreams up in his laboratories. They thrive on love, and love is transmitted, among other things, through music. If you give plants love, I thought to myself, be they vines, or roses, or marguerites on a balcony, you will be surrounded by a forest that will never leave you and you will smell its perfume wherever you are, even when you leave the country and immerse yourself in the fumes of the city. And in that forest there will be colour: the colour green, the colour blue, the colour of the sky, the colours of the sunset. A life without colour is a life that will lead nowhere because it will always be flat. If you nurture a passion for life and for nature, the colour that surrounds you will flow into you, fill you, accompany you as you experience the daily cadenza that is the land, that is life on the land, that is love for the land.

Tarantola was going to be my music – a Jazz Wine Vine Fusion.

Eventually the end of three years came and the last contract binding us to our sharecroppers was terminated. We were penniless, but free. Free, what an incredible feeling. Free from everything and everyone, free to be able to do what we wanted without negotiation. Free to determine the future of Tarantola.

However, the first harvest without the support of the sharecroppers was going to be a test. I took on some of the sharecroppers as employees, the ones that were willing, and hired a small group of men from Alcamo to supplement the team. All went well, better than I could have hoped, and the yield was satisfactory.

The last day of harvest is always a joyous moment – you celebrate with the workers, you laugh, you joke, you drink wine, you roast *salsiccia* on the grill. I bought a great quantity of meat, ordered the fire to be lit and sat waiting for our harvest feast to start. When the men came back from the fields their faces were strained. They gathered round the fire without a word, clearing their throats and looking at the ground to avoid my gaze. Only one of them spoke. He informed me that none of them were in the mood to celebrate because this was their last working day. They were making themselves voluntarily redundant, after only a few weeks.

'What? Why?'

No explanation.

As I looked around the taciturn group, some of whose faces I had known for years, I felt as if I was hallucinating. How could every single one of them be leaving, all of them, in one fell swoop? What had I done? Of all the landowners in the region we treated our workers the best (I really believed that). It was a blow and it fell with a heavy thud.

The men ate their meal, leaving large chunks of meat untouched on their plates, and then left. As I stared at the empty chairs scattered around the smoking fire one man, the dearly beloved and never to be forgotten Damiano, came up to me.

'Not me. I will not leave. I have always worked for the Testa family. The day I stop working for the Testa family will be the day I stop working forever.'

Damiano had been a sharecropper. He came from a large family of sharecroppers and lived, as they all did, in the heart of the country. When I announced that I was terminating the sharecropper agreement, he came to me and told me he that was giving up his vines immediately – effectively handing them back to us. He didn't come to me with sob stories, he didn't try to haggle for money like most of them did, he asked for nothing in fact. Instead, to my surprise, he told me that he had cobbled together his entire life's savings and bought a little plot a few hectares wide adjoining our vineyards.

He was a beautiful man – statuesque, tall, with a smile that, for some reason, made you feel instantly calm. He went everywhere on horseback. He had a handsome black stallion that accompanied him into the fields every day, ploughed his land, and lived in complete symbiosis with him. He owned a small stock of animals, made his own cheese and grew his own fruit and vegetables. Everything he laboured over flourished, everything he produced spoke of his passion for nature – perfectly formed tomatoes; heavy, juicy melons; everything. Even the simple act of placing vegetables in a basket was undertaken by him with phenomenal care. He was a person of presence, and although he was a simple man he was cultured. A man of the old world and the new.

Damiano was scared of nothing – for him adversity was something that would always be overcome. A bad harvest meant only that you could smile and say: the next one will be better. Damiano instilled a sense of security in me. I felt protected and I knew we could work alongside each other with mutual respect.

'But how will we work the land, Damiano, if we don't have anyone to work it?'

'Don't worry. We will find people. We will work harder. We will finish late, but we will finish. You just have to make a decision – keep going, or throw in the towel.'

I couldn't have had a worse start to running the family business. I had put my shoulder to the wheel and thanks to my efforts the farm had been completely abandoned. Well done, I said to myself as I walked back to the house, very well done, compliments on your outstanding achievement.

Later that night the fears returned, gnawing at my mind like rats, and I couldn't sleep. For the first time in many months I suffered a vicious attack of stomach cramps. But in the darkness, almost in the centre of the pain, I could feel a strange force beginning to take hold. The more I was being pushed away from the land, the more I was drawn towards it. An incomprehensible, magnetic push and pull.

During one of those famous Sunday lunches, lunches when all the family got together in Palermo, my father-in-law told me that he had spoken to a priest who was well known in Alcamo. The priest had mentioned an agronomist – an expert in the science of soil and crop management – who was working on some new initiatives funded by the region. This agronomist, apparently, had asked to meet me. I nodded in response, with the enthusiasm of an animal that has a noose around its neck and knows it is about to face the knife. I felt as if the ground was slowly subsiding beneath my feet, but I agreed to meet him. Maybe this was my last hope, to speak to an expert, someone who might actually be able to help me.

We had an appointment in a restaurant in the Piazza d'Alcamo. He arrived breathless and as red as a peperone because he had rushed there from an inspection at one of the farm projects he was supervising. We talked about everything except agriculture. The more the conversation went on, the less he talked about anything that I was interested in. At the end of the lunch, like good Sicilians, we started to walk slowly along the Corso VI Aprile, one of the main streets in Alcamo. It took us almost two hours to walk eight hundred metres. Every three steps someone stopped us to say hello, or to chat, including the priest my father-in-law had mentioned – a personality in Alcamo at that time. The hand-kissing abounded.

Eventually, after another good half-hour, I managed

to get some sense out of the agronomist who told me that he could probably do something for me but that first he needed to come and see the land, and then he would decide what the next steps should be. Our meeting ended late but I wrung a visit from him for the following day.

At five in the afternoon we met on the estate. We walked around the old vines and the bare empty fields, saying almost nothing. After what felt like a very long hour we stopped by the long, stone, nineteenth-century horse trough in front of the farmhouse.

'I've never been here before – what a wonderful place.'

His eyes were sparkling. I was in with a chance.

Suddenly:

'I know you want to sell. I know there are people hovering around, people who want to buy.'

'Not at all. I have no intention of selling. I've had offers but frankly they were insulting, and at the moment all I want to do is rebuild this place, replant the whole lot. I have come to you to find out if you think there is any hope.'

'There is hope. A new ruling has just been passed in Sicily granting young farmers soft loans with an almost ridiculous interest rate: 2 per cent to be repaid in fifteen years. All you have to do is to submit a project, and, if it's approved, start the work.'

My legs were shaking; I could hardly get the words out of my mouth. I had finally found someone who could throw me a lifeline. I asked a thousand questions. He replied that he would tell me everything I needed to know, he was ready to discuss it all, but that we would have to talk in his office at the end of the week. We said goodbye.

I drove back to Palermo at full speed and told my mother. She turned her nose up at the idea, saying that it was too much of a risk. She was right. It was a risk. But, as so often in my life, risk felt like the only security.

The following days were full of anticipation. I postponed all work engagements in town so that I could spend every minute of the day in the countryside. I wanted to be on my land, to feel the earth under my feet, to smell its smell, to touch it, to dream about its rebirth.

I climbed the hill behind the farmhouse in the grip of a fever. As I reached the highest point I looked down the valley. The vineyards are indented in the centre by a narrow gorge and vines rise out of the gorge on either side – two furred humps scored by perfectly symmetrical lines. I stared at the view and at the earth below me, the sticky red-ochre clods, the little wild flowers, the unkempt scrub grass waving about in the winds of the tramontana. Everything was beautiful, and everything was waiting.

The end of the week approached. As agreed we met in the agronomist's office, on the third floor of an old building with an inconspicuous entrance accessed from a narrow side street. First I had to announce myself at a makeshift reception area. I was accompanied down a strange arrangement of corridors leading to two small rooms lined with filing cabinets. In the second room, sitting behind the door, was Andrea, the agronomist, dwarfed by a large neat desk with a small collection of framed awards making a halo behind him.

He began very slowly, in a faint voice, to explain the project to me. He showed me some papers about the new law. I couldn't take much in, but I heard that we could dig an irrigation lake, that we could replant the vineyards, and that if I was in agreement he would take care of the whole thing. Surveys, plans, designs, drawings, everything. I said YES, YES and YES. I decided not to wait for my mother's permission, I had decided for her. At the end of the meeting he shook my hand. 'Have courage. I will take the project on and I will work quickly.' He said that he would need documents and signatures and that he would be in touch.

I believed in this man. He seemed rational, thoughtful, he had the air of a scientist. I sensed an uncommon intelligence. Finally I held in the palm of my hands a seed, a plan, difficult to administer but achievable.

For the next few days I felt elated. I learned about the new plants on the market – the different varieties, types of culture – I wanted to do something unique. But soon I was in a state of depression again because Andrea did not get in touch. Days passed, very long days, without news. I didn't dare ring him in case I disturbed him, or possibly because I didn't want to hear him say that he had yet to start on the project, or, worse, that he had changed his mind and didn't want to be involved any more.

After a month the call came. He was going to assess a forest on Monte Pellegrino in Palermo, could we meet somewhere en route? 'Certainly,' I replied, and drove to meet him with a pumping heart. When I arrived he greeted me with a small gesture of the head and opened the boot of his white Fiat 131. He pointed at a pile of thirty or so enormous documents.

'This is your project. Are you going to take it to the regional office or am I?'

'My project? What? You've finished it already? Why in God's name haven't you rung me all this time?'

His reply was cryptic: 'I had other commitments.'

I put everything in the boot of my car and sped to the regional office to get there before it closed. I went through all the red tape, with as much patience as I could muster, and came out staggering with emotion just as the security guards were locking the gates.

Once I had submitted all the paperwork to the regional office I became unstoppable. I worked every hour of the day, somehow juggling my software commitments with meetings setting up the new project. I knew hard times were ahead, but I felt totally and completely alive.

On Saturdays as always I drove from Palermo to the countryside to pay Damiano, our one remaining worker. Not exactly an onerous task, but an important one nonetheless. One Saturday, a few weeks after my meeting with the agronomist, I arrived at the entrance to the estate to find a surprise waiting for me. Our lovely, tree-lined drive was swarming with sheep, at least a hundred of them. Not only that, someone had created a sheep pen on the drive, surrounded by huge fences, which you could only pass through via two gates – one as you went in and the other as you left. To get to the house I had to first open and close the gates of the estate, then drive up to the pen, open the pen gate, drive the car through, get out, close the pen gate again, crawl through the dense, whining flock sounding the horn so that I didn't crush the animals to death, open the pen gate at the top, drive through, get out of the car and close the gate behind me.

Beyond the last gate a shepherd – I supposed he was the shepherd although I had never seen him in the area before – was standing on the drive looking determinedly away from me. I walked over to him and asked what was going on.

'Well, you weren't around, and the sheep were feeling a bit hot on the mountainside, so we brought the pens down here, temporarily.'

'And how long exactly is 'temporarily'?'

'A few weeks maybe – we'll probably take them back up in a month.'

It was obvious how much respect he had for me, the owner of the land. Then he asked a question.

'Anyway, what's the big problem if you have to sell?'

'What? I have to sell? No, I don't have to sell.'

'Oh, you don't understand. You do have to sell.'

Everything was becoming clear. I walked away with the words: 'I'm thinking about it.'

So that I should understand a little better, somebody started helping themselves to things on the farm. First it was the antique furniture in the farmhouse, then all the machinery in the yard. Then there was a fire, which by pure miracle didn't quite destroy all the barns. In other words, a persuasive little campaign. With each new semi-petty incident, the same force continued to wedge itself inside me like a splinter – something much more useful, this time, than rage. Defiance.

The proposal for agricultural project funding was processed, the authorities inspected the land at Tarantola, and it seemed that everything was in place. It was 99 per cent certain that the grant would be approved. But no one knew when it would be approved and I was impatient. I wanted to build myself a model farm, I wanted it at any cost and I was beginning to realise that to achieve what I wanted to achieve in the environment I now found myself in, I had to have a strategy.

A company had been earmarked to complete the land works should the funding application be successful. After numerous phone calls, I managed to track down the owner of the company and meet him in a bar, a bar that neither of us normally frequented. I explained the situation, as discreetly as I could, and I asked if he would consider putting his men on the job early while we were waiting for the grant to come through. After several meetings, always in the same bar, he agreed.

A huge gamble – what if the grant fell through at the last moment?

It was July. I decided to move to the country with my family, including my mother, who insisted on coming along to organise the move despite the fact that she had been against the project from the beginning. She was strangely silent, offering neither criticism nor encouragement but reassuring my wife and children with her gentle presence.

In mid July a construction site was set up – we were digging an artificial lake in one of the fields below the house. The kit was impressive: four excavators, two diggers, an infinite number of trucks and an army of labourers – the rumble of machinery on the farm was like thunder. Never has the dust, billowing in the air around the house, seemed so sweet. It was like setting off on a marathon without knowing if you would ever get to the finishing line, but I wasn't thinking about the danger, I wasn't thinking about anything, I just wanted the smoke signal to be witnessed, the message to be received loud and clear. I wanted 'them' to understand that the wind had changed.

Casual questions back in the sheep pen: 'So, Conte Testa, where did you get all the money?'

Then one day I noticed cars drawing up to the gate at the bottom of the drive and turning away again at top speed. Be careful, I thought to myself. Be very, very careful. You haven't seen anything yet.

The Mafia – a bunch of thugs who will sacrifice anything and anyone to achieve their verminous goals, a bucket of worms, in fact, in the hands of a single fisherman. There is always one mafioso at the top of the heap, a single mind that drives the swarm, but you hardly ever see his face.

Cosa Nostra, as the Sicilian Mafia is known, exploits the poor. It sucks the poor dry. It deploys the poor with the illusion that by putting their lives on the line they will get rich while in reality the only thing they have to gain is an early death or, if they are lucky, a lifetime in prison.

The family unit is the source of all things good, but in Sicily it can be the source of evil. The direction of a child born and brought up in Sicily depends on the begetter, the one who gives life. If a child is taught that good can be born out of evil, then he or she may choose to take the right road. But when a son is born into a household in which the father passes down evil, from the moment the boy first puckers his mouth to suck from his mother's breast, the boy will take on the characteristics of his father and follow him into the darkness.

In the 1980s, the fortunes of Cosa Nostra were taking a turn for the worse. A new generation of policemen and investigators were making a determined effort to expose the Mafia and bring the most violent offenders to justice. Facts were uncovered such as the existence of an organised hierarchical body that operated internationally, a fact that had been denied by the Mafia for years. Certain members of Cosa Nostra were becoming extremely agitated and initiating a counter-campaign that was more ruthless than ever. People involved in anti-Mafia activities were assassinated, some of them in broad daylight in front of their wives and children.

One of the investigators making a name for himself at the time was Giovanni Falcone. Falcone was a young magistrate who possessed a searing intelligence and a level of integrity that was rarely seen in the legal system. He managed against all the odds to bring some of the most influential mafiosi to trial. During his famous 'Maxi Trial' alone, 360 mafiosi were brought to court and, even more unusual, convicted. Falcone's fearlessness in the face of the Mafia not only made him a star on the international stage, it filtered into the Sicilian public consciousness. For the first time in many decades Sicilians allowed themselves to imagine the unimaginable – that the powerful but mysterious, blood and honour-bound organisation that was Cosa Nostra might one day be defeated.

Meanwhile, a war was going on in Alcamo between two mafioso families – the local, ruling Rimi family and the Corleonesi. Friends and family members of the Rimis were murdered, and power was slowly but surely changing hands. The power struggle came to a head with a vicious battle fought out with sawn-off shotguns on the streets of Alcamo. Many (apparently) innocent people were killed in the crossfire, and the Corleonesi came out victorious.

I was expecting a visit at any time.

One morning, just after the battle in Alcamo, two men about forty years old turned up at Tarantola wanting to speak to me. I recognised one of them – I'd spotted him a few times wandering around the estate. I met them in the yard, away from the house, and they launched in without so much as a '*Buon giorno*'.

'Listen, lad, you have a family, a little daughter, just born, you need to come round to the fact that it would be better for you to sell. Our buyer has a proposal for you.'

A smile passed fleetingly over my lips, like a cloud in a strong wind. 'Let's hear his proposal. I'm all ears.'

The proposal was an offer of 200 million lire, instead of the billion that the estate was worth. They told me that they would give me a month to think about it, but only because they respected me.

'Thank you, *signori*, for your respect,' I replied. 'We will meet in a month then.'

They sauntered back down the drive, throwing their cigarettes into a bush as a sort of punctuation.

Play for time – that was the only thing I could do. Play. Improvise.

Just as I stepped back into the house I received a phone call. It was Andrea telling me that the grant had finally been approved – the first financial building block was in place. 'That's good news,' I said, looking at a dust cloud on the hillside kicked up by one of the tractors.

More tractors lumbered onto the estate and just as the rains arrived we began to deep-plough the earth, preparing it for the cultivation of the new vines. I will never forget the smell of that earth, as the ploughs' blades sucked it up and out of the ground. It had a particular smell, the smell of resurrection. After years and years of complete neglect, our estate was starting afresh.

It so happened that, as soon as we finished ploughing in readiness for the new vines, the final harvest of the old vines began.

Against all the odds, the vines that stood on the little bit of earth that was still cultivated squeezed out buds, contorted their branches under the hot sun, lifted their heads up against the humidity and spat out their last crop. A record crop – both in quantity and quality. The Catarratto grapes, native to our Alcamo hinterlands, understood. They sensed that it was their last year, and they wanted to leave the world giving me the strength to carry on. I looked at the heavy bunches – some green, some golden because they had been more exposed to the sun – and my whole being concentrated itself on the vines. Words came out of my mouth, thank you, almost inaudible.

Damiano and I started the harvest with three labourers: three African men who had no idea that there was an embargo against working at Tarantola. I gave them all board and lodging and kept them on the estate so that they couldn't be got at and persuaded, by good means or bad, not to work for me.

There was one other labourer – a casual named Carlo. He was a local man who came in for the odd day to man the heavy machinery. Carlo was an acquaintance of Damiano's – it seemed they had known each other from childhood. He was small, swift, and brown-faced, and he kept himself to himself. He had a reputation for being a good shot and he would often turn up at the door with a brace of rabbits or pigeons – knowing, no doubt, that he would receive a child's weight in prize vegetables from Damiano as payment. He hardly spoke to me – on the contrary, he made it clear that he was working not for me but for Damiano, and that under duress. If he was with us for a day he started early, before anyone else had had their coffee, and left well before sunset – not because the work was finished but because he had decided it was time to leave.

Damiano, three labourers and an occasional shift from Carlo was not enough to get us through the harvest, so I thought to myself: there is only one thing left to do – go straight to the lion's mouth and enlist the sons of some of the 'foot soldiers' prowling around me, the clowns employed by our local ringmaster to keep watch.

There were three of them – I often encountered them on the road, or hanging around in a bar in town. Two were on the scrawny side, roughly shaven; one was muscular, with a deep scar on his right cheek. He told me that he had cut himself on some barbed wire while he was working on a farm. I didn't believe that little story.

They were slippery creatures. They looked at you with the arrogance of the worldly-wise, as if they knew everything, as if you were worth nothing. They had been born into a culture that taught them that the only way to get ahead was by creaming off the profits of others – stealing, plundering, collecting protection money. But despite their bravado and assumed confidence, the molecules of poverty were flowing through their veins, into and out of the pores of their flesh.

At first they were taken aback by my offer of work, but concluding I suppose that I was a city boy and therefore 'uninitiated', and realising that they could earn a bit of easy money, and, more importantly, that they could use it as 'cover work', they accepted. I took the muscular boy on to drive the grape truck, and the other two to drive a tractor and pick grapes. I managed, with some careful manoeuvring, to keep them around me for most of the day – particularly the truck driver who had to sit around waiting for a full load of grapes to take to the winery.

Those who are with you, you can keep your eye on.

The countryside has a hundred eyes. Look for them as much as you want, you won't see them. But they see you. From the hillsides they watch you, everything you do – they see when you leave home, when you return, who you are with, if you have children, if you are with your family, if you aren't, if your friends have arrived, or if they haven't. If you're alone. Especially if you're alone, because when you're alone you're vulnerable. People in the countryside never watch out of curiosity, curiosity is for the city. In the countryside people watch for a reason.

The boy with the scar was in a lot of trouble with the law – so bound up in badness in fact that I didn't know if he would appear from one minute to the next. He clocked in for work later and later each day, but with a bit of application I managed to keep him with me for the entire harvest. He was the leader of the pack and the others feared him, probably because he was the most violent and in the criminal world that is what counts. I turned my attention to him and started a programme of slow, inexorable brainwashing. One day I broke the unspoken rule and talked about his 'alliances', suggesting that robbing and easy money would only create problems for him. He told me to mind my own business. But I wouldn't let it drop, and as the days went by and the boredom kicked in and the beer became more plentiful and the shadows of the evening longer, our conversations deepened. I managed to get him to open up a bit. He started to boast about his evil deeds and I listened and nodded. 'Well, you've got balls, I'll give you that.' By now he was confiding in me. A coffee, a panino, and then I invited him to lunch at the house. Every so often I would ask him if he really wanted to follow in the footsteps of his father, his uncle, his cousins: in and out of prison, forking out cash for a pile of crooked solicitors. After a month I noticed a slight change in him. Now we were no longer taking coffee alone, the other two would join us and they would jabber away about cars or computers, as boys do.

The weather had been exceptionally wet and the harvest was lasting a lot longer than usual. I had just heard that the regional office was ready to pay for the next stage of works, so I suggested they sign up for the whole winter.

Meanwhile, the buyer's representatives were becoming more threatening. Raising their voices, they warned me that they had waited long enough and were losing their patience. I persuaded them to give me another six months, saying that by then I would have finished the project and they would be buying the land with the vines replanted. All I wanted was a small hike up in the price they'd offered me in recognition of the fact that the land was going to be restored. We agreed to go to solicitors the following spring.

So, I asked, could I at least know who the buyer was?

The reply came: 'You will know him soon enough.'

I couldn't wait to look him in the face, the man who was pulling the strings of all these puppets.

Winter arrived suddenly, soon after our olive harvest. Winter in Sicily is mild and lasts for a very short time – a few days of rain, a few days of cold.

The regional project funding had finally come through and been transferred into my account, so in January I settled my bill with the contractors (to their enormous relief) and ordered the new vine shoots – 200,000 of them. Within the space of a day, farm labourers were coming to my door, falling over themselves to work for me – for some reason the embargo had been lifted. In a fit of enthusiasm, and without asking myself why there was suddenly and inexplicably no embargo, I signed up fifty men.

I was still working in Palermo but I took the Monday off to oversee the first day's work. The trucks arrived, as planned, at eight o'clock loaded with vine shoots, their roots cradled in small, hard pockets of earth. The plots that were due to be planted were marked up with string into straight lines with root holes at regular intervals – the grid created was as neat as if it had been drawn by a robot. Each vine shoot was lifted out of the truck, carried to its place in the line, planted, heeled in, watered, and its tiny tendrils fed onto the lowest wires for encouragement. By the end of the first day the hillside behind the farm, which for weeks had been a blank expanse of earth rising up to the sky, was transformed into a highly organised pattern of green dots.

I went back to Palermo that night with my mind full of possibility and slept like a baby. The next morning

I was woken at 5 a.m. by a call from Damiano. Half the vines we had planted the day before were missing. Obviously I took another day off work and drove to Tarantola to find out what had happened. I was met by a gathering of labourers milling around the horse trough, waiting for the go-ahead to start work. I got out of the car and walked over to Damiano. Nobody knew anything, he told me – the best thing was to finish planting the field we had started the day before and order more plants. I agreed and phoned the order through straight away, watching as the farm workers headed up through the vineyards for another day's lifting and digging and securing and watering.

At the end of the day Damiano and I walked the hillside and checked each plant. Everything seemed to be in order. The new plants were winking in the late-winter light. I drove back to Palermo.

That night I didn't sleep, and when Damiano rang me at 5 a.m. I was ready for the call. More plants missing, nothing seen, nothing heard. It was the perfect cycle: we planted vines during the day, during the night they were uprooted.

This time when I arrived at Tarantola I encountered two of my young friends, the truck driver and the tractor driver. As I passed them I gestured to the half-empty field in front of us and said to the boy with the scar: 'This isn't right.' To my utter astonishment I heard him reply: 'No, it *isn't* right.'

Once again I had to cancel all engagements and decamp full-time to the country. My business partner informed me, in no uncertain terms, that unless this was my last unofficial holiday he would terminate our contract. Then my wife announced that she and the children would not be coming to the farm at the weekends. We discussed it and I agreed that it would better if she and the children stayed away from Tarantola. As I walked to the car I remembered my father's words to my mother: 'Bebè – business is not for you.' I had always thought of them as the words of a patriarchal man, steeped in the traditions of an old society. Now I was beginning to detect new notes, new meanings in his words, new tones in the memory of his voice. Maybe this was what it was to grow up – to understand the true meaning hidden within sentences spoken in the past.

Damiano arranged another rota of workers, limiting the numbers to those we knew and trusted, and we took it in turns to guard the fields at night to ensure the vines weren't being lifted under cover of darkness. At the same time I continued to make lunches for the three young men. They started talking about girlfriends, about wanting to marry, about travelling to London or New York, saying they were tired of the life they were living. They told me that they had asked their parents why I was being targeted since I was giving them work. I had derailed them and I was overjoyed – not because I had manipulated them, but because they were starting to talk about changing their lives.

At last we finished planting the new shoots and, whether it was because we were guarding the territory or because local 'orders' had changed, the overnight thefts stopped. There was only one thing left to do, and that was to destroy the old vines, the faithful old plants that I had inherited from my father and that had saved us from ruin in their final year.

Destroy. That word sums up the feeling of uprooting a vine. One of the most horrible experiences. The plants look at you, they know their end is near. They have given you their all for twenty or thirty years, but, as with everything, there must be a beginning and an end. Memories of magnificent harvests – grapes given to us by the vines, rich in colour, ripe, full of must and sweetness. All those smells, all those aromas, stripped out by some terrifying mechanical shovel and carried off by a bedlam of tractors. A piece of your life leaves you. You will never live that time again. There are good times to come but you cannot know, imagine, feel, hear what does not exist. Although maybe you can sense it, in the silence, in the silences, you can touch it if you try, the flow, the course of a new life, of a new plant, a hundred, a thousand, hundreds of thousands of little vines ready to bring you back the dream called nature.

After the destruction came more ploughing, in preparation for the final phase of the project. Deep ploughing: the earth clawed out of the ground, sharp blades entering into the soil more than a metre to tear out the dark subsoil, turn it upside down, and pull out the old roots.

Winter rainwater gathered in the naked furrows, feeding the ground with moisture, preparing it for spring.

Nature is a cycle
A terrible cycle in which the strong rule always over
the weak

Always?
No
There are animals that escape death
By dint of an active intelligence
And a dose of improvisation

They run
They don't think about where to place their feet
They know their feet will hit the ground
Conviction gives them strength
They never give up and
If they fall, wounded,
They pick themselves up again

Man kills not out of necessity but for pleasure
Every day he commits acts of violence
Unworthy of nature
Against his own fellow man

If you are surrounded by nature
Life assumes a different hue
A different shape
The expression of life changes
You receive drops of happiness
Just enough to quench your days

۴

FOUR

Spring arrived and the new farm was taking shape. One irrigation lake was completed and filled to the brim with green water, and all the diggers moved on to a new site to start excavating the second lake. Labourers were erecting canes in the fields all over the hillside ready for yet more vines. I took on additional workers to help lift and carry because I needed to finish as quickly as possible. The project was almost complete.

But I was in torment. Time was passing, the moment of reckoning approached, and sooner or later I would have to look it in the face. Indeed, late in the spring I received a phone call arranging an appointment with the ringmaster himself.

I was going to meet the man who had orchestrated the whole campaign. I started to think, to plan what I wanted to say, even to write down notes. Then I decided: no, I will improvise. I will weave my way into the wilderness, I will decide how to respond and what to say in the moment.

A sleek black car, with a scrappy-looking vehicle leading the way, turned into the drive. I wasn't quite shaking, but almost.

Two stooges got out of the battered escort vehicle and looked around.

Then he got out of the car behind.

Tall, dark sunglasses, dressed in black as if he had recently suffered a loss. Shoes polished to within an inch of their lives. A more than ample belly. An indescribable appearance.

Finally. Facing me. The head of the Family. The Puppet Master.

We sat down. He removed his sunglasses. But he didn't look at me.

Eyes fixed on the horizon. Fixed.

I poured the coffee that Damiano had prepared. He drank it without a word, holding the cup with his little finger cocked in the air. Sitting at a table with someone who says nothing, who stares into the distance and treats you as though you are completely insignificant, is an uncomfortable experience.

I waited for him to finish his coffee, I didn't touch mine.

I waited for him to speak, I had nothing to say.

'Good,' he began. 'I knew your father, an honourable man. I hope that you will prove to be worthy of him.'

I wasn't sure how to answer. 'I am doing my best and will continue, always, to do my best.'

'I'm glad you understand,' he said.

'Understand? Understand what?'

'That the moment to sell has arrived.'

(Oh yes, I understood, I understood only too well).

'And indeed I will sell.'

He smiled – a sneering, sardonic little smile.

'You know, boy, your land really isn't worth anything any more. The offer we've made you is more than generous. All you have to do is go to the solicitor. Everything will be paid when you sign.'

He spoke with such arrogance and certainty that it was difficult to move, let alone speak. I was sweating. But not a word came into my head. Only music. John

Coltrane. 'The Love Supreme'. I was in love with my land. And now that I had, opposite me, the very man who wanted to pluck that land from me, I felt the love grow, become a passion, and passion makes you blind.

'Yes, I will sell, but with one small modification. You are offering me 200 million lire. Now that I have replanted, I want two billion.'

A glacial silence.

His gaze twisted itself away from the horizon and he looked straight at me. His eyes were ice. Welling up with hate. Thirty interminable seconds.

'That was not the deal,' he said.

'The deal was that I would sell after I had replanted. And I will sell. I always keep my word. All you have to do is agree the price.'

I was pushing him into a corner, catching him off guard. No, he hadn't expected this. I was keeping my word, to sell; he wasn't keeping his, to buy. He told me that I was playing with fire, and that I would be burned.

He stood up, his gaze slithering back to the horizon, and said: 'We will meet again soon.'

He got into the black car and the wheels of the convoy lurched into action, spitting out fountains of mud behind them.

It was over.

I could consider myself a dead man.

But I was happy. Just as when I was at the piano, improvising had made me feel safer. Not giving in had made me stronger.

A silence like the silence of the tombs fell on the countryside. Not even the birds, the little birds that normally thrilled the vineyards with their daily song, were singing. It was as if nature herself sensed the presence of evil.

I walked over to the horse trough. I could hear the spring water trickling into the trough, trickling away without end. A sweet sound, full of life. I drank a palmful of water; I needed it, my mouth was dry and bitter with bile. The water had a particular taste, fresher than ever before.

Damiano, who had made himself scarce until now, came up to me. He could tell that it hadn't gone well. He put his hand on my shoulder. 'Courage,' he said.

His hand was as heavy as a boulder. Courage?

There was only one certainty. If they were going to do anything it would be sooner rather than later, within the next week, or two perhaps.

In the following days I saw shadows everywhere. I was sure I was being followed, watched. I was in a state of total paranoia like a taut rope that was being pulled to its absolute limit.

My first instinct was to run back to Palermo, to pretend to my family and friends that everything was normal, to hide myself somewhere in the mess of the city's ancient, dirty streets – but of course I knew that was impossible. I had to stay in the country, to oversee the final land works, and to watch for any malicious attacks on the farm.

I lingered in front of the farmhouse as the labourers arrived, partly to see if there was any change in their behaviour towards me – there wasn't – and also to see if the three young men would turn up. I didn't know what I was dreading most – meeting them, which would mean talking to them, or not meeting them, which would mean that they were complicit in the whole affair. I looked for the three faces that were now so familiar to me among the groups of men arriving in dribs and drabs, some on foot, some by car – but they were nowhere to be seen.

Two days after the honoured visitation and halfway through the excavation of the second lake, the largest of the diggers broke down. Some local mechanics took it apart in a desultory fashion – as if they had no expectation that it would ever work again – and then abandoned it. It stood like an omen, leaning at a comical angle by the half-dug crater.

I had cameras installed around the outbuildings and set up security lights on every side of the house. I suggested to Damiano that he move into the farmhouse for the remaining weeks of the project and slept in one of the spare rooms, and he agreed. With Damiano around I felt safer – I could hear his steps around the house, and listen to his unruffled voice first thing in the morning and last thing at night.

I invited Andrea to visit the farm and stay for a couple of days. Anything not to be alone. He was complimentary about the progress of the project and talked excitedly over breakfast, lunch and dinner. I tried to give the impression that I was paying attention, but in reality I was listening for something else – small, unusual disturbances in the air or the sound of cars arriving, or leaving, when they shouldn't have been. All I could hear was the scratch of a cricket on the terrace, the call of a scops owl, toads croaking in harmony in the open countryside.

A week passed and, other than the fact that the digger was eventually put back together again and continued its mindless tunnelling, which was in itself a miracle, nothing out of the ordinary happened.

I started to relax a little, to make calls at night without fearing the echo of my own voice in the room.

A nother week went by and there was still no sign of trouble. As no works were planned for a couple of days, I put Damiano in charge of the estate and set off back to Palermo to see my wife and children.

It was a beautiful late afternoon in May, and when I drove away from the farm my spirits lifted a little – the winding, half-melted road that led from Alcamo to the main highway was quiet, the sun through the windscreen was warm but not hot. Vines and olive trees lined the road, their leaves bright with spring rain.

As I approached the road to Palermo I noticed blue lights. I slowed down. There was a police car blocking the slip road. When I asked what was going on, the policeman I spoke to looked uncomfortable – he clearly didn't want to give me any explanation but said that there had been an 'incident' and that if I was intending to drive to Palermo I had better change my plan and go back to Alcamo, or wherever I had come from. I turned round, taxied back into town – also quiet – and headed to the nearest bar for a coffee. If in doubt, stop and have a coffee.

There were a few people in the bar – it was a little after 6 p.m. All, including the barman, were perched on stools with their eyes glued to the screen of a small television hanging precariously on a shelf above the counter. When I walked in they ignored me. They were watching the news – reporters talking with the self-important intensity that reporters adopt after a serious event. I saw images of a highway – the road to Palermo I assumed – tarmac blackened and torn, upturned vehicles and debris strewn across the road, litter and papers blowing about in the wind, a small crowd, a battalion of police. The reporters were asking, surmising, conjecturing, and then, finally, confirming. There had been a bomb attack on the highway just outside Palermo; two cars had been destroyed and many others hit, at least five people were dead, including the object of the attack – Giovanni Falcone, Sicily's most famous, most effective and most idolised anti-Mafia investigator.

Nobody spoke, I certainly didn't think of ordering a coffee. I left the bar and walked back to my car. Falcone dead – it was inconceivable, unbearable. And unquestionably a disaster – not just for me, but for anyone who had had the guts to defend themselves against the daily, increasingly dogged advance of the Mafia, especially in the west of Sicily where the new mafioso boss, my friend Mr Shiny Shoes, had recently been shoring up his power base.

I drove slowly back to the farm. The roads were even quieter than they had been before – no, they weren't quiet, they were deserted. I arrived at Tarantola and walked up the steps of the farmhouse, calling for Damiano. He was not in the kitchen, not in the dining room, not in his bedroom. The front door was unlocked, some of the windows were open and creaking in the wind. Where was he? Maybe he'd heard the news? But how would he have heard it? Maybe he was also in a bar watching television? But he never went to bars. Maybe he was in town? Pointless questions. For want of any better ideas, I decided to head over to his house.

Damiano lived in a tiny old homestead on the edge of the estate. It consisted of one storey, with a brown metal door at the front and two shuttered windows at the back. Its brutally simple exterior was softened by a climbing rose that framed the entrance, and by an ordered little garden that surrounded the house and gave it the feeling of an oasis. On one side of the house, tufted vegetables were laid out in thick lines – tomatoes, aubergines, beans, onions, garlic – and on the other, brightly coloured flowers grew under a row of lemon and orange trees. Damiano's house was comforting to look at, as always, but it was decidedly empty, and although the garden had been watered – possibly even that very morning – it was clear from the state of the cobwebs around the front door and on the shutters of the windows that no one had opened them for a while.

I had to think again – the light was beginning to go and the emptiness of the estate was stultifying. It was evening so I was not expecting to see anyone working the fields, but the stillness of this evening had a particular quality. It crossed my mind that I should find Carlo – Damiano's childhood friend and sometime worker on the farm – to see if Damiano was with him, or ask if he knew where Damiano was, or to find out if he had heard anything.

I wasn't sure if I would remember the way to Carlo's house – it was many years since I had even driven past it. He lived with his wife and family near the small hillside town of Camporeale. Most of his children had flown the nest but I believed he still had a daughter living with him. The idea of seeing him at his home was intimidating – I knew what he thought of me – but now was not the time to worry about that.

I decided to take the back roads, not because they were safer, in fact they were usually quite the opposite, but because I was more likely to bump into someone who could give me information – a farmer travelling on foot, making his way somewhere or coming back from somewhere. The road was rough, as it always was in the wet season, and in some places deep mud made it almost impassable, but I crawled up the hill and down again, up another hill, and down again. After taking the wrong turn several times in the descending darkness, and reversing back out of numerous dead ends, I came across a village I knew, drove through it and finally found the track leading to Carlo's house.

There were lights on in the windows – someone was home.

I drove towards the house and instinctively parked a little distance from it, although I was certain that whoever was at home would have heard me arrive. I got out of the car, knocked tentatively on the flaking wooden slats of the front door, and felt the pressure of a tiny movement somewhere inside. Then the door opened by a crack.

'Signora Maria?'

The woman was middle-aged, dark, short, bird-like. She remained silent.

'It's Signor Testa – from the farm at Tarantola. Is your husband here? I wonder … I'm looking for Damiano.'

The magic word – Damiano. Why did he leave such an impression on us – this simple man of the country, who had never travelled, or made money, or done anything other than grow things, which was, after all, what most people in the country did?

The door opened and I was invited into the middle of a room divided into two sections – kitchen and living area. Although the light was quite dim, I could see that the place was spotlessly clean. Signora Maria stopped by a wooden table but didn't sit down and didn't offer me a seat – letting me into the room was clearly as far as she was prepared to go.

'Signora Maria, I'm so sorry to disturb you. Especially on a night like this. But … I thought your husband might know where Damiano was … or might be with him in fact.'

She shrugged.

'Have you seen Damiano? Have you seen your husband tonight, Signora Maria? Have you heard the news?'

She gestured to the wall, a bare stretch of rough plaster, and said: 'Carlo is hunting.'

'Where did he go, Signora Maria?'

There was no answer, and there was not going to be an answer. Tight-lipped. That is what we Sicilians are called – tight-lipped because we never tell. We never speak out.

So Carlo was out 'hunting'. There was no point waiting for him – the only thing I could do was to return to the farm. I gave Signora Maria my thanks, which she received with an almost imperceptible nod of the head, and walked back to my car.

I drove away from Carlo's house in a state of confusion. I had no idea what to do, what to think – the end of Falcone, it was like the end of civilisation, and the chaos that was bound to ensue had not yet begun.

It was dark but I drove with my headlights dipped, which was nearly disastrous because coming down the hill I skidded very close to a precipice. The physical danger didn't seem to matter much. As I climbed back up towards Tarantola I stopped the car and got out to walk. I could see better in the open air – the night was clear and an iridescent moon lit up the dirt track in front of me. The curling tendrils of the vines were brown and silver – I had seen these vines planted, I knew the smell of this earth, I knew the exact line of the vineyard with its grooves and its wires, I knew the curve of the olive groves on the hill. I was on familiar territory.

A movement on the soil took me by surprise. It could have been a fox, a rat. I stood still. There it was again – this time a step – the pressure of a heavy foot on the soil.

Another step.

'Filippo?'

?

'Filippo?'

Damiano's voice.

'Yes! Yes it's me! Damiano – for the love of God!'

'Sorry to frighten you.'

'Damiano, thank goodness you're here.'

'We should walk. Keep walking.'

'Yes.'

'To the hut above the house – by the eucalyptus tree.'

'OK.'

We walked across the soft ruts of earth under the vines, taking care not to garrotte ourselves on any of the cross wires. Eventually, after what seemed like an age and my shoes had almost entirely filled up with soil, we reached the hut. The old metal door was broken and jammed half open. Once inside, we let our eyes adjust to the dim light, both, I imagine, looking around to check that we were alone.

And so the explanation began.

Damiano had been with Carlo. Damiano knew where Carlo was now. Damiano seemed to know everything, but maybe everyone in the countryside knew everything except for me.

When Damiano heard the news about Falcone he also went to visit Carlo. Why? He wouldn't say, except that he thought that Carlo might have some 'information'. Carlo didn't exactly have information but he sat down with Damiano and told him what he was going to do. Had I heard about Carlo's daughter?

No, I hadn't heard about Carlo's daughter.

Damiano told me that she had been assaulted. Carlo knew who had done it, and suspected that one of the reasons for the attack was that he, Carlo, had recently been working for me.

'For me?'

'There was an embargo, as you know.'

I had been so wrapped up in my own world over the past months. It hadn't crossed my mind that someone working for me or associated with me would have been subject to that kind of attack. Maybe I hadn't wanted to admit it to myself.

Carlo knew about Falcone's assassination. Carlo had said to Damiano that Falcone's murder was going to change everything.

Damiano paused and was silent for several seconds. Then he continued, carefully.

Carlo had said that enough was enough. He was a man of honour and he was going to avenge the assault on his daughter, and many other things besides. After that, he was going to give himself up to the police and tell them everything he knew.

I felt sick to the stomach. My big, brave project seemed suddenly very small and insignificant.

Damiano told me that it was time to return to the car and drive, not to the farmhouse but to Alcamo, where we could both stay with his sister until the roads were clear and I was able to go, finally, to Palermo to see my family.

I stayed the night in Alcamo in Damiano's sister's apartment, as he suggested. I rang my family as soon as I arrived – everyone was shocked but fine. Damiano, his sister and I ate a simple, subdued meal together, talking about my parents and old times, and retired for the night. I slept on the sofa – a short, disturbed sleep.

An hour or so later, the unmistakable sound of gunfire woke me. At first it was several streets away, a few shots muffled by the thick walls of the old town. After about fifteen minutes there were more shots, this time with less reverberation, possibly coming from an open space, a piazza, close at hand. There was no movement in the street below – or in the building, or anywhere in the apartment – only that strange suspension you feel in the city when violence breaks out under cover of darkness, and a hundred ears listen, and nobody moves.

The next morning Damiano's sister made no mention of the night's disturbances. She insisted on giving me breakfast although I wasn't hungry. Damiano apparently had already eaten and gone out on an errand. I thanked her profusely and stepped into the street. The morning papers were plastered with reports of Falcone's assassination, but there was no mention of an incident in Alcamo. The bar on the main square was full of workers. All heads turned as I walked through the door, and then quickly reverted to their default position, eyes down on the table or the counter. I drank an espresso and left as quickly as I could, intending to return to the apartment

– Damiano's sister had a television so I thought I might find out more by watching the news.

She was out when I got back, but she had given me a key so I let myself in, sat down on the old sofa and switched on the television, with the sound off. Images of the highway – taken from the same angle but with fewer people in the frame and less chaos. The tarmac was a mess – it was clear that the highway was going to be closed for a very long time. Then another news item flashed onto the screen, another murder. This time the victim was the local mafioso boss.

I turned up the volume and watched, transfixed. His appearance was unmistakable. The black suit, the shiny shoes, the belly, the glacial stare. Don Alfonso, the ringmaster, had been shot. No suspect as yet but a full investigation under way. Talk of another power struggle taking place in the region – various incidents the night before, shootings, arrests, information coming in minute by minute.

A power struggle, if I was lucky, might grant me a short period of remission. A new Mafia regime would spend time regrouping and then establishing itself. A new regime would have new priorities, new ambitions, new friends to make and, most importantly, new enemies to fry.

The telephone rang. I left it for a few seconds until it crossed my mind that the call might be for me. It was Damiano's sister. She was with a friend and would be out for the rest of the day, maybe also the evening – her friend was very nervous and wanted company. Damiano, she said, had gone back to the farm to make sure that everything was secure but he had asked her to tell me that he thought it would be safe to drive to Palermo, via the back roads.

The air in the apartment was lifeless. I went back out into the spring sunshine and, instead of getting straight into the car, I walked along the uneven, paved streets that I knew so well and found myself in the Corso VI Aprile. Instinctively I entered the church – the Chiesa dei Santi Paolo e Bartolomeo.

The church was lined with candles, hundreds of them, candles in red vases, candles in green vases, loose white candles leaning precariously on recesses in the walls, candles stuck with wax onto narrow stone ledges, balanced onto the arms of the saints, dripping onto the pitted marble palms of their hands. Secret flames, secret thoughts, licking the stone with their tongues, licking the walls with their light and illuminating the Alcamese baroque: columns of red marble, a huge canvas depicting the patron saints, the stuccos of Vincenzo and Gabriele Messina and the frescoes of Antonio Grano.

I sat in one of the pews and thought about Carlo. I thought about his wife, Signor Maria, and about their daughter. I thought about Damiano, a man who had retained his sense of self in the midst of everything and had never wavered.

After a while, bewitched by the beauty surrounding me, I heard it. Silence. That same silence that I had heard standing among the family vines before they were destroyed, intoxicated by the fruits of their last harvest.

Grape must
An unforgettable smell
It contains everything
Your days
Your hours
Your passion
Your love

The sun and the moon
The stars

Grape must
An unforgettable smell
It speaks of hot days
Speaks of fatigue
Of great joy but also of pain

It enters you
And possesses you
Before leaving you forever
To become wine

۵

FIVE

The following three years were demanding, but calm. Every August I decamped to the country, accompanied by my mother. My mother, who a few years before had implored me to sell, who disapproved of the fact that I had applied for government money, who was disappointed by my fractured career and bemoaned the fact that I never sat down at the piano, who made no bones of her dismay when she learned that I was spending less and less time with my wife, my mother was becoming proud. Proud of her son, proud of the land she once wanted to disown.

During the second August at Tarantola I had an unexpected visit. Late in the afternoon on an oppressively hot and humid day, a day when stray dogs lay in the road in heaps, a car that I didn't recognise drove very slowly up to the farm. I saw it approaching in the distance – in those days we had few visitors, generally only the farm workers ventured into the vineyards and even the post had to be picked up from town because the postman refused to drive into the Alcamo hinterlands simply to deliver a letter.

The car was a Fiat – I don't remember the model but it was shiny and new, probably the reason for the slow approach. The Fiat drew up outside the farmhouse and out of it stepped a young couple. The man was stocky, with thinning hair and a weak goatee beard. The woman was well dressed and immaculately made up. The young man approached me with a confident smile, and it was only then that I recognised him – Liborio, one of the three wayward youths that I had employed on the farm, the youths that disappeared after the ringmaster came to call. Liborio was one of the scrawny ones, but he had gained weight, and an elegant girlfriend to boot.

'Filippo. How the hell are you?'

As if no time had passed, as if nothing had ever happened.

'Filippo, let me introduce you to my wife, Daniela.'

'Delighted to meet you.'

As custom demanded, I invited them both to take a coffee on the terrace. The young man sat down and looked around. 'Just like old times, eh?' I nodded. I thought it would be better to keep silent and let him explain the reason for his visit. Instead he turned to his wife and started describing his time as a 'farmer' – the harvest, the people, planting new vines, taking coffee with Filippo on the terrace, the laughter, the conversations – as if he were describing a holiday. She listened attentively, but was seemingly unimpressed.

Eventually I decided to make a couple of polite enquiries.

'So, Liborio, what are you up to now?'

Liborio was clearly glad to be asked. He had, he said, started a new business in Alcamo: car sales and repairs. He had secured a generous loan and already business was good – this year alone he had sold thirty cars, both new and second-hand. He fished out a business card and assured me that if ever I should need assistance he would attend to me personally.

'And how is your father?' I asked.

The young man poured himself a glass of water and then, taking his time, he poured a glass for his wife.

'He's good. He's OK. Things are quiet.'

'And your friends, the ones who were here working on the farm with you?'

He made a small unmistakable gesture with his hand.

'Prison?'

'Yes. Along with her father.'

There was an awkward silence and Daniela blushed. I asked her how long her father would be in prison for and she replied: 'For life'.

A thought came to me. That morning I had been shopping – a big shop, food for a week. I got up from the table, went into the kitchen and opened the fridge. There were four large lumps of cheese on the shelf – fresh cheese, the very best quality, about a kilogram each in weight: primo sale, pecorino, caciocavallo, ricotta. I took them all out of the fridge and put them into a bag, then I walked back onto the terrace and handed the bag to Daniela.

'For your father, when you visit him.'

All of a sudden the atmosphere changed. Daniela immediately stood up from her chair and hugged me. A strong, prolonged hug. When she sat down again there were tears in her eyes. Liborio laughed. 'Filippo. Always the same Filippo.' He understood perfectly – the gift was a flirtation, a thinly veiled compliment to his wife, but it was also a calculated move. Those who are with you, you can keep your eye on.

After a while, the two made their excuses, wished me well and walked back to the car, depositing kisses before they left. As the car drew away I stood at the top of the terrace steps and watched it disappear. I stood there for many minutes – thirty minutes, maybe an hour. I was thinking about the significance of the visit. Certainly, it was a gesture of respect. Liborio wanted to show off his new wife (why wouldn't he? – she was beautiful) but he also wanted me to know that he was now in charge of his own destiny, keen to be visible and to establish a network of personal contacts. As I ruminated, a twinge of pain shot through my stomach. Only a twinge, a memory of something past.

Liborio had been the least assertive of the three young men, the least noticeable. But often the people who stand out most when they're young make nothing of themselves, while in the background a quiet few watch, and learn, and slowly build their empires.

There is nothing more lovely than seeing a vine grow. Tending it, day by day, cherishing it like a baby, helping it grow healthy and strong for one year, two years, until at last you reach the summer of the third year – the year of the harvest.

Finally the third August after the new planting arrived. Everything was going well: the vines were full of grapes. The old wooden supports had been replaced with modern wire espaliers, and all you could see from the terrace in front of the house was an incredible sweep of green. It looked as if it was going to be a record harvest – the plants were strong and the weather was ideal. Since spring we had had steady temperatures, no rain, and the right combination of winds – sirocco and tramontana – raging at times but always gentle at night. The vines had been literally rocked to sleep, and their flowers had metamorphosed into plump, fully-formed grapes. Perfect. Everything was perfect.

But I could tell that my mother was hiding something from me. My mother suffered from arythmia and had been to hospital several times for check-ups. She said she had occasional bouts of pain but nothing more. In the middle of August she told me that she wasn't feeling well and that it would probably be better for her to go back to town just in case. I knew that it wouldn't be wise for her to drive to Palermo so we decided that she should go to the hospital in Alcamo. I asked a friend of the family if she would accompany my mother because I still had a lot to do in the vineyard.

It was seven o'clock in the evening. I was standing on the hill watching the sun turn, the earth of Tarantola absorbing the colours of the sunset. I felt a sharp pain, near my heart. I thought it must be something in my ribs, or that my stomach was playing up again. Darkness entered my mind. I decided to walk back down the valley to the house and call the hospital to see if everything was all right. I heard the telephone ringing in the distance. News about Mamma; the results of the electrocardiogram weren't good and they had decided to transfer her to the hospital in Palermo because it was better equipped than the one in Alcamo. It was suggested that I meet her there, in Palermo, and also that I should prepare for the worst.

When I arrived at the hospital I found my mother in bed, lifeless. I stared at her, she was smiling, she looked extraordinarily beautiful and serene. I turned away, I wanted to remember her like that always. Caterina, Contessa Caterina, she had left us. No, she had left me. Right at the moment of renewal, the moment of recovery, after so many years of effort, years of suffering, just when we were daring to hope for a new future.

A new future. She had wanted it for so long. Maybe she preferred to observe it from above.

The harvest arrived without me even noticing it. Damiano, who was now officially the farm manager at Tarantola, organised everything. The first grapes to be harvested were the Damaschino – a complex variety that produces a high yield but is extremely vulnerable to disease. During the harvest I like to be among the harvesters, in among the vines. Even I was taken aback by the first rows – I had trampled up and down those rows a thousand times. I had picked off hundreds of leaves because they looked as if they were diseased and might infect the whole crop. But the grapes were perfect. The harvesters were smiling at me, they were part of it, this amazing crop – a veritable mountain of grapes, all of premium quality.

Damaschino – an unbelievable yield; even today I remember the satisfaction that vine gave me.

Inzolia – so delicate, with an unmistakable snow-white must, a fine grape.

Trebbiano – big long bunches, a full, weighty fruit.

Catarratto – prince of the Alcamo DOC, a noble grape cultivated and savoured by generations of Alcamesi.

Chardonnay – even in the first years of production, delicate, furtive little bunches concealing within themselves a great wine.

Nero d'Avola – the king of the reds, aristocratic, handsome, imposing.

The vines were heavy with the weight of the grapes – how was it possible that my mother wasn't there to rejoice with me? The grapes were so fat and healthy and full of must it was almost as if they had been kissed by God. Blond, flawless, ripened to perfection, every lorryload dripping with juice. I had never seen anything like it.

It was an extraordinary harvest – forename Caterina, surname Resurrected.

A drop
In the sky
Light
In the dark
Red
On white
Gold
On a black label

SIX

It had taken four years to prove that I could run the farm at Tarantola. The abundance of the first harvest impressed the farm workers and I could feel that there was a change in attitude towards me in the countryside. The farm had been rebuilt and Damiano gathered together a small team of labourers that we knew we could rely on. There was every reason to be optimistic.

There were two changes I still had to make. The first was a step towards independence on the wine market, a step that many Sicilian wine producers were taking at the time. The second was a fundamental change to the way we were farming the land.

Once the first harvest of the new vines was over, I started the process of predicting future yields and calculating the farm's profit and loss. I was troubled – we were producing a large quantity of grapes and yet the business was making almost no profit. The family had lived on the proceeds of the vineyards for years and, in the past, my father had been satisfied with even a mediocre harvest, so how could the profits be so small?

The Sicilian cooperative system was part of the problem. The cooperative wineries, although at first they helped lower production costs, were suffering from a few years of willful mismanagement and becoming not a support but a threat to small producers.

During my father's time in Alcamo there were 1,000, 2,000, maybe even 3,000 people producing wine – a lot of families with direct access to the market. When the harvest was over, everyone stored their wine in tanks underneath the houses until the annual wine market took place in the Piazza di Alcamo. Wine brokers moved around the piazza, promoting grapes from different sources, managing sales, all in the hope of getting a good commission. The wine market was fragmented but it was robust: if someone went bankrupt they were a tiny fly in an ocean of wine. The cooperative wineries took away that stability, seducing farmers with the idea that a million hectolitres of wine combined and sold as one lot would have more bargaining power on the global marketplace.

By the fourth year of operation at Tarantola the banks were putting pressure on me, but the idea of surrendering after investing so much was unthinkable. Instead I decided I had to increase the value of our product. Gorgo del Drago is the name of a dry river running along the edge of Tarantola, running deep into a gorge on the edge of a precipice. Gorgo del Drago was the name given to the first vintage wine with the Conte Testa label, borne of the conviction that the only way forward was to bottle our own wine.

It was another step in the dark. Friends and acquaintances inadvertently spurred me on, telling me that, naturally, my problems on the farm were far from over, but I had made a wager and it was going to take more than a couple of harvests to win it. Go to the devil, I thought, do I need to be reminded?

I started with 10,000 bottles as a trial. I commissioned a new label and drove the designer mad because I changed my mind every second. Eventually we produced a label *sui generis* – a stain of colour on a deep blue background which could be interpreted in a thousand different ways. To some it suggested the lava of Etna; some saw nothing but a blob on a dark background; to others it conjured up the colour of the sea at dusk. Exactly what I wanted – a label that was odd and intriguing. On the label at the back of the bottle, the number of the bottle and the words 'Year Zero' were printed.

At the end of January I loaded ten cases of six bottles into my car and, instead of asking experts to judge, I gave each bottle to a friend or acquaintance and asked for nothing in return except their opinion. I knew that sixty bottles would be enough to tell me either way. The responses came in. The wine was good they said, not of the first class, but good.

Gorgo del Drago was launched onto the market at a ridiculously low introductory price. Every bottle sold.

I remember a spring afternoon in the late 1990s, an afternoon of unusual stillness in the Alcamo hills. We were spraying the vineyards with a chemical compound that prevented disease, mainly downy and powdery mildew.

We treated the vineyards for a period of fifteen days every year. There was no rationale behind the spraying – chemical treatment was a custom that happened whether or not disease was present, a custom most farmers in Sicily observed without question. Added to the cocktail of chemicals were pesticides that attacked the grapevine moth, a tiny insect that was capable of destroying several tons of grapes in a matter of days.

On that particular spring afternoon I was following the tractor to check that the spray was falling as it should. I saw bees, bees that were no danger to the vines at all, falling by the wayside. Hundreds of bees and hundreds of other insects with them, no insect that the chemical touched had any hope. At that moment it struck me that we were driving down a dead-end road.

Once again I started reading and researching, making enquiries about alternative methods of disease prevention that were being trialled elsewhere. I decided to cut down the number of treatments on the farm and devised a programme of gradual chemical reduction over five years that would allow the vines to get used to receiving less treatment or, in some cases, to receiving none at all. The transition happened slowly, but with considerable anxiety on my part. A virulent attack of mildew can be fatal to the crop.

Organic viticulture was the final and maybe the most important risk I took at Tarantola. This time I knew it would be many years before I would reap the rewards. Organic farming has advantages. The first is economic. You can charge more for your produce and save the considerable amount you would have spent on chemicals. But the appeal for me was not economic; it was the idea of establishing a closer connection to nature.

Prevention rather than cure is the rule in organic viticulture because once a disease has inveigled its way into the crop it is almost impossible to combat. As soon as the first buds come out of hibernation and start producing shoots you have to monitor the vines, checking them ideally in the early hours of the morning.

The love of flowers that was handed down to me by my mother turned out to be my saving. Roses are the organic vineyard's natural alarm, because disease will attack roses before it attacks the grapes. I redesigned all the flower beds on the farm and planted an endless number of roses. The following May there was an explosion of colour on the estate – yellow, red, white, purple, streaked, scented, unscented roses were blooming everywhere. The most delicate roses were the ones I paid most attention to and with a little bit of practice I learned to intercept a mildew attack before it reached the vines. Walking up and down the vines in the early morning, examining the roses, the vine leaves, and the tiny, budding clusters of grapes, I learned to judge whether or not the time had come to spray.

Copper sulphate is one of the few synthetic substances available to organic farmers to tackle mildew. You have to spray at night – we usually start at two in the morning, on a night when there is absolutely no wind. Sometimes it feels like a cruel hour, but climbing to the top of the hill at Tarantola in the middle of the night is an experience not to be missed. The tractors move fast so that they can spread the sulphur as quickly as possible and as they pass a cloud of deep blue blooms in the air – engulfing each row one by one. Despite the rumble of engines you can almost hear the plants breathing in the cool of the night. They stand perfectly still, perfectly in line, but you can sense their movement, their rhythm.

The rhythm of John Coltrane.

The plants bow their heads but they don't suffer. Any human being walking around without protective goggles, however, finds their eyes streaming because a large quantity of sulphur in the air irritates the eyes.

As the night progresses, the tractors progress – up and down, up and down they go – and then everything stops, and the tractors disappear, and you remain.

A rustle of wind every now and then reminds you that it's May – the time of the sirocco, the wind that comes from neighbouring Africa. Or maybe it's the tramontana, the wind that comes from the North. Or maybe a bit of one and a bit of the other – the perfect combination for the first flowering.

And then

You sense nature
You sense her inside you
Embracing you
An outpouring
Of shade
That melds you with the leaves
You do not fear
Because you feel that you are not alone
You are surrounded by the kind of love that only nature is capable
of giving
You become a part of her
She has faith in you
Not even the birds are singing
There is only the silence
And the moon
And a sky streaked with galaxies in relief
And the smell of sulphur hanging in the air
And a rustling
And you listen
To a night on a dark hillside
Foxes and nocturnal animals surround you
They hear you breathing
Nothing comes near
Birds of prey fly between you and the moon, leaving you with the
impression of a painting, the oils still wet
The houses of Tarantola lie below, in the distance
Small
The first glow of dawn
It's time to climb again

To the highest point
Fatigue
Sweat
But also anticipation
The birth of another day in the vineyard
Another day that God has blessed you with
Running the last steps
Panting
You reach the summit
The sun emerges behind a cluster of grapes, and sticks to you
It will not leave you for the rest of the day
Everything becomes translucent
A thousand colours lit up
Pills of light, drops of heat
Who said that solitude brings anguish?
Solitude tempers you, teaches you, takes you on a journey
Solitude doesn't exist in the middle of the vineyards, you never
feel alone
The vines embrace you, a green embrace
They leave specks of dust on your arms which, like a book,
recount their story
Their birth, the moment of grafting, the pain of the first pruning,
the joy of the first harvest
Pride in their gift, the gift of satisfaction to the deserving
The joy of growing near you year after year
Suffering and crying out only when they feel the slice of the shears
Like the cotton pickers' plants
Pruning is an art
You need to know how to prune without making the vine suffer
One day as I was cutting a plant to make a cleft graft
I spotted old graft wounds low down on a trunk

A pruner explained to me the difference between the wounds
A cut made with force, and a cut made with love
Yes love
The love that you bestow on nature and nature bestows on you,
little by little, in small doses
The love that picks you up in the morning and travels with you
into the evening
Never making false promises, never misleading you with false
illusions

The vine is there
Giving you its wine
Still alive in the bottle even when you're asleep
Alive
Always alive

And when at first light of day you walk back down the
hill, it seems a shame to leave the night behind, and you
wish that it would never end.

Filippo Testa

Filippo Testa has been running his family estate, the Conte Testa vineyards in the Sicilian Alcamo doc region, since the 1980s. Over the years he has established an organic wine and olive oil business (Gorgo del Drago), a guest house, and a traditional Sicilian restaurant and cookery school. Before taking over the family vineyards, he was a computer programmer and spent several years playing and recording as a jazz pianist in Palermo.

Susannah Elliott

Susannah Elliott trained at Bristol University and the Royal Academy of Dramatic Art. She worked as an actress for ten years before moving on to a career in the heritage sector. She now researches, writes scripts, and produces interpretation for exhibitions and historic houses. She lives in London.